Kid Fit for Fun

KidFit
for
Fun

Written and Illustrated

by

Erin Crain

Kid Fit for Fun
First Edition Trade Book, 2020
copyright © 2020 by Erin crain

To order additional books:
www.amazon.com
www.kidfitforfun.com

ISBN: 978-1-952943-03-4

Book Design and Hand Lettering: Erin crain
Layout: Julie Lucas
Editorial and Book Packaging: Inspira Literary Solutions
Printed in the USA by Ingram spark

Dedication

My dad used to say, "Keep me posted on all the cool stuff." Dad, this is so cool! You would have loved it. Thanks for being my greatest fan here on earth and in eternity.

Acknowledgments

Firstly I would thank Nik Lehnert for his continual guidance on this journey. If he didn't suggest getting a journal and writing down what I was teaching the kids, there would be no book. Nik thank you for continually reminding me that what I was creating was worth publishing. I am grateful that you encouraged me to stick it out and for all the times you challenged me to try again. As you know this has not been an easy endeavor.
You have been such an encouragement.
Thank you.

Thank you to Blake and Shannon Casteel and Tiger and Carrie Hill for being in my corner and championing me through this journey. You are all some of the dearest friends of my life and have been pillars to lean on as I journeyed through the hard season of losing my father. Thank you for believing for me in the hard moments and fighting for my breakthroughs. Thank you for encouraging me to step out into the dreams of God over my life. You all have taught me what healthy marriage and family look like and helped me become a greater woman of God.
I am grateful for covenant!
Love you guys!

Thank you to Keitha Crain, my mother and my loudest cheerleader. You and dad always believed that each of us kids would do cool things, and prayed that we would know and follow God.
Love you more than goo goo plex!

Thank you to my Crain family for being patient with me as I have endeavored in missions to walk out the call of God on my life. Thank you for loving this book in all of it's stages.
Thank you for believing for the finished outcome.
I love you all!!

Acknowledgments

Madison Hudson. You are a dear friend. Thank you for believing in this dream. You were the first person to get behind this vision and sow financially so I could purchase essential supplies to start this project. Your generosity built so much faith in me to believe I could do this.
Love you friend!

Thank you to my Respect the Corners community for rooting me on in this endeavor and coming around this vision of kids fitness. Thank you to all the coaches that jumped in and helped cover classes while I was sick. It meant a ton.
Love you RTC!!

Thank you to one of my hanai mamas, Julie Lucas for introducing me to our local art store, and the gift card to get a few more supplies there. Thank you for championing me in my creativity and for helping me get this huge book to a digital state so I could get it published. Thank you so much for the many hours you took to help me in this final stage.
Love you mama Julz!

Thank you to Rick and Kae Olson for also sowing financially so I could get supplies when I had run out. Your gift was timely and I am grateful.
Thank you for believing in this vision.

Lastly and most importantly, Thank you God for showing me that this book was your idea. I could only begin pages when I could see them in my head. Thank you Lord for all the cool ideas. Thank you for encouraging me to take risks. Thank you for the boldness to try things that were creatively out of my comfort zone.
Your ways are always better!

Table of Contents

Foreword

As I read KidFit for Fun, I am reminded that I never had anything like this as a kid. What Erin Crain has done with this book is nothing short of inspiring. She is a woman full of integrity, who is constantly serving as other people's greatest champion. In this book, none of that changes.

Not only does this book teach kids and parents fun ways to move correctly and experience different types of workouts, it brings the joy of all kinds of different "fun facts." Erin gives kids the opportunity to not only learn about fitness, but brings nuggets about sharks, tongues, water, and even funny bones that make this book far more enjoyable and creative than one would think a fitness book could be.

My absolute favorite part of this book is Erin's rawness with the loss of her dad. She is vulnerable about components of life that some people would rather not talk about: pain and grieving. Erin gives kids an opportunity to learn how to process these things through faith in Jesus. She makes it very clear that the only way she has overcome the pain of a death of a beloved parent is through the gospel of Jesus Christ. This is what truly gives us all hope! Matthew 5:4 says, "Blessed are those who mourn, for they will be comforted." (NIV) Erin has proven this true. She writes from the comfort of Christ.

I believe the kids and parents who read this book will be filled with excitement for fitness and overcoming challenges. My advice would be to give everything you can to walking out the activations from this book. Not only will you increase your fitness, but you will begin to realize that you can overcome anything!

Thank you, Erin, for giving this book all you've got! You always give everyone all that you've got. This is what sets you apart.

Blake Casteel
Founder, Respect the Corners

(Respect the Corners is a functional fitness movement out of YWAM-Kona in Hawaii.)

Introduction

I want to invite you on an adventure. A pilgrimage of how this book you are reading came to be. This was a personal journey of overcoming, where out of my pain I would create something to be proud of.

I didn't intend on writing a book. I didn't know that this kind of creativity was in me. I felt empty. I had just experienced one of the greatest heartbreaks of my life that left a pain sitting on my chest. The pain that comes from missing someone so much because you know you'll never see them again. Pain has a tendency to get stuffed down deep and can go undetected for quite some time. But when it surfaces, it can feel like a lump in your throat. I felt like I could burst. I wished that I could have just run away from the pain. And that pain was more than I could bear.

I had been a CFL1 trainer a year when some close friends approached me with a thought. Knowing the natural gift I had of working with kids, they encouraged me to attend a crossfit kids specialty training course. I had started seeing a new dream realized through the avenue of crossfit and working with kids.

There happened to be a kids' seminar I could attend on the way home for christmas 2016. My heart came alive at the training course as I realized this was something I could see myself doing with my life. I shared this new-found passion with my family over the holidays. I was most eager to share with my dad! Dad always had a way of being super passionate about the new things that my brothers and I would try. And with my dad's health declining, sharing this dream would be special. I knew this would be my last christmas with him, and that was hard news to take in. I just didn't know how much time we would have left with him.

In a few short months I would fly home again to tell my dad that I loved him for the last time, as he went to be with Jesus. My dad was one of my best friends and my biggest fan!

The months that followed were a blur, and a deep depression set in. If I hadn't had a good community around me, and my faith in God, I don't think I would have ever have come out of the fog. By the grace of God and those around me holding my arms up, I found what I needed to embark on this endeavor with kids' fitness.

Four months passed without my dad as I started my first fitness class at the learning center, a school in my community. I still had moments of weakness and felt like I failed every time I stepped out. I wanted to quit before I even started. I wished I could go back to the kids' specialty course, because the pain I was feeling was snuffing out the enthusiasm I'd gained there. But there was something deep within me that whispered, "It's okay, you can do this." These words, and the feedback I was getting from parents about how much their kids were enjoying my class, put wind back in my sails. I felt like I was coming alive again a little bit every day.

A few weeks into coaching kids' classes, a friend of mine, whom I've looked up to, encouraged me to write down what I was teaching the kids. He is always learning and making himself a better coach. He currently has his CFL3, which is a big deal in the crossfit world. Because of this, and his encouragement, I take what he says to heart.

So I went out and bought a journal to keep track of what I would teach the kids. I was just doodling in my journal. I wasn't planning on showing it to anyone. My first few pages were something special. I would sit on my bed, going through my new drawings, and had a sense of pride. I would have thoughts, "What if they wouldn't like it?" "What if it wasn't good enough?" But I kept finding myself sitting on my bed in awe of what I was creating. By taking time to draw out what I was imagining in my head, I found a life-giving outlet.

So, I shared my journal, those first early pages with my family and a few trusted friends. Everyone was blown away and said it was "GOLD," and that I needed to publish it. This did something so deep in me. These words began a healing work in my heart.

The thought of my journal becoming a book added a lot of pressure. It went from being a fun outlet to me thinking it had to be perfect. I was too intimidated to even start a page some days, in fear that it wouldn't be good enough to publish. Progress stopped for several months, because I saw it as a chore. It wasn't fun anymore. Writing this book was never my idea and I had to wrestle that thought out. I believe this book was God's idea. Once I came to terms with that, the pressure lifted and it became fun again. God was guiding me and He would give me the inspiration for these pages.

I've been in missions for seven years. As I was writing this book, I kept thinking about the refugees of the world and the foster care crisis in America. I knew I had to be an answer. And I thought, "What if I had a tool to reach the marginalized? What if I could train and send out coaches to reach the youth and affect entire families? What if my book could be that tool?" Everywhere you look there are kids. All the kids of the earth have a similar longing. They all want to be seen. They want our attention. They want to be known.

As I was in the process of writing out these workouts, I knew it couldn't be just another app on our phones. I wanted something tangible, something durable that you could hold in your hands, something interactive. I grew up with my dad reading out loud to us kids. My desire in writing this book is to draw families together. I hope this book will be an encouragement for all of us to be present so we don't miss pivotal moments right in front of us. We can't get them back.

I can't believe it has already passed the one year mark of me buying the journal that started it all. This is the first time in my life that I have been determined to finish what I have started. I have always quit when it got hard. It was just easier. In my mind, if you didn't commit, you didn't fail. So much has changed in my heart. Even though I've been through struggles with my health this last year, and the heartache of losing my Dad, I am determined to finish what I have started. I have even dreamed about trying other things now.

I am convinced that it is important that I invite others in so they too can let beauty come from their ashes. I have come to realize that beauty comes from pain. Without trial, there is no growth. Without challenge, there is no victory. We will face adversity in this life. The question is, "How will you respond to that adversity?" Our response matters. What we do with the life we have been given sends out ripple effects. How we choose to live out our life matters. You matter. I want to tell you that whatever you are going through, you too can overcome. I want to invite you into a life of dreaming. I want to invite you to simply try the thing that most intimidates you. And on the days "you don't feel like it", reach out and ask for help.

So, as you hold this book in your hands, keep in mind that it is an invitation. It is an invitation to believe in yourself, to believe that you can do the hard things. You, too, can overcome.

This book has five chapters. Each chapter builds on the one before like you are walking up steps. It begins with foundational movements and ends with more advanced skill work. You will see some of my favorite movements, as well as tons of fun facts to inspire you as you step out and try new things. All of it is designed to challenge you and to build you up. You don't want to build anything on a faulty structure. We need a firm and strong foundation.

Our foundation is what establishes our belief system. Why do we believe what we believe? What we believe about ourselves will shape the trajectory of our lives, whether good or bad. If we have a healthy belief of who we are and what we can accomplish, we will succeed in life. But if we don't believe the good about us, we won't do anything with our lives. This will only lead to a destructive lifestyle.

We were not designed to deal with negativity in our lives. We were designed to be champions and to thrive. I believe the latter can be accomplished by four foundational pillars: Family. Faith. Integrity. Love. These pillars brought me through the grief of losing my dad. These pillars have absorbed the shakings of my circumstances and given me a firm place to stand. These pillars are the foundations of the book you are reading. I will share more about each of these life changing pillars and the importance of them in our lives at the end of each chapter.

The workouts you see in each of these chapters are doable for all ages. scale and modify according to your need or child's need. children should not be unattended while doing these workouts. when it calls for team or partner workout as a parent or guardian, jump in. This is a fun way to interact with your child.

There are many pictures in this book with weights on barbells. This feature makes the picture more fun. start out with a pvc pipe, dowel, or light weight till you see excellent and ideal form. Then, as you mature with the movement, begin to add weight slowly over time. learning the proper way will also avoid injury.

As you read on, you will see the breakdown and the fullness of this book and its intent. From the simple to the most complex of movements, the effort you put in will determine your results. Every day, we are given opportunities. whether we try and succeed or try and fail, what matters is that we try. some of my greatest victories have come from failure. My hope is that by sharing the things that have helped me, you might find some tips that do not only challenge you to get fit but help you overcome hard things too.

Thank you for joining me on my journey. I hope you enjoy embarking on yours!

let's get moving. stay safe. And have fun!

Erin crain

Author's Note

The following terms and acronyms are found throughout this manual and are explained below:

page 16
EMOM
every minute on the minute

page 26
AMRAP
as many rounds as possible

page 42
"chipper"
complete the repetitions of the first exercise before moving to the next

page 90
AMRAP
as many rounds as possible

chapter

[1]

foundational movements

There are
9
foundational
movements

- They are natural multi-joint movements.
- They are the building block for most all other movements.
- They are useful for every day life.

These movements have 3 levels and build upon each other as you progress from level 1 to level 3.

Squats : 1. air squat
2. front squat
3. overhead squat

Presses : 1. strict press / shoulder press
2. push press
3. push jerk

lifts : 1. deadlift
2. sumo deadlift high pull
3. medicine ball clean

1

foundational movement
air squat

Deck of cards workout

✳ 3 ◆ = 3 Haulers

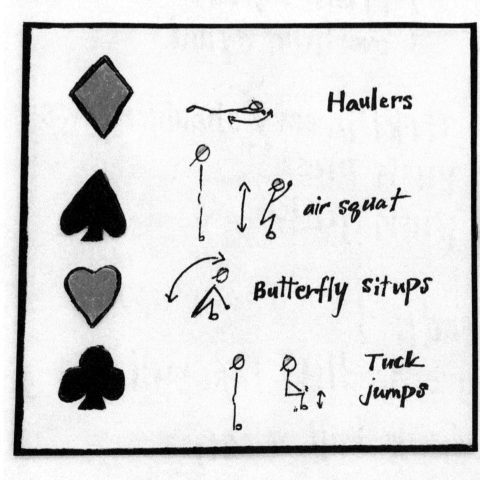

◆   Haulers

♠   air squat

♥   Butterfly situps

♣   Tuck jumps

challenge:
face cards worth ten count on each movement.

Water is a very important part of our body as we need it to live.

fun fact

Water should be awarded the most valuable player as it helps do so much in our bodies.

Here are just some of the things water does:

- helps deliver oxygen all over the body
- regulates body temp
- flushes waste out of your body
- lubricates joints
- forms saliva to help digest food

Drink More Water

Our Bodies 60% Water

Brain 75-80% Water

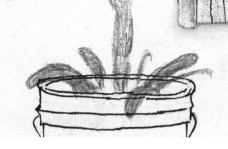

2

foundational movement
front squat

Keep those lazers high!!

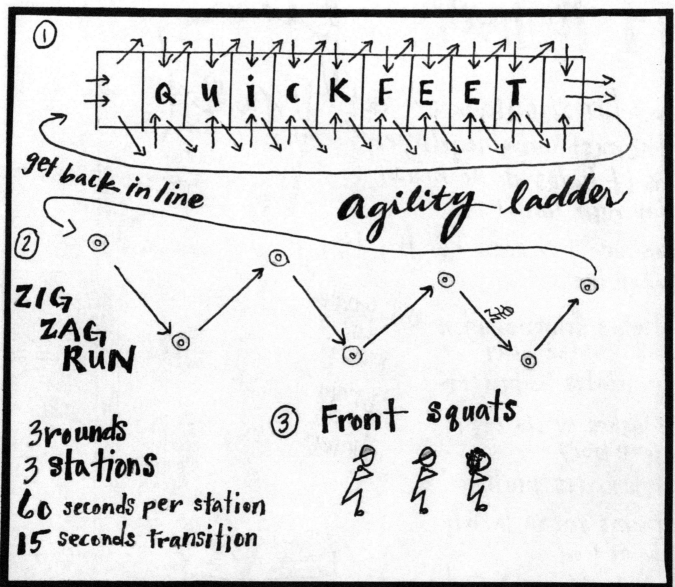

① QUICKFEET

get back in line

agility ladder

② ZIG ZAG RUN

③ Front squats

3 rounds
3 stations
60 seconds per station
15 seconds transition

blood Type

A | AB
B | O

The +/- is called the rhesus factor, with + being dominant, and − being recessive.
* If both parents have negative blood, the kids will also have negative blood.

Our blood is special and we need it to sustain life.

Do you know your blood type?

Here is a chart to find out.

	Father's			
	A	B	AB	O
A	A/O	A/B AB/O	A/B AB	A/O
B	A/B AB/O	B/O	A/B AB	B/O
AB	A/B AB	A/B AB	A/B AB	A/B
O	A/O	B/O	A/B	O

(Mother's)

Here are some possibilities.

fun fact

3

foundational movement

Overhead Squat

- shoulder width stance
- wide grip on bar
- shoulders push up into bar
- armpits face forward
- hips descend back and down
- hips descend lower than knees
- Lumbar curve maintained
- heels down
- bar moves over middle of foot
- knees in line with toes
- stand

6 min Amrap

5 OH squats pvc pipe

10 box stepovers

Turn around

This movement requires balance.

- you are taller in the morning.

- you can't tickle yourself.

- when you take a step you are using 200 muscles.

The masseter is the strongest muscle

STRANGE

Did you know that we all have unique functions in our bodies?

fun   fact

- your nose can remember over 50,000 smells.

- There are 500 sweat glands in your feet. your feet produce about a pint of sweat per day.

- Throughout your lifetime, the amount of saliva you produce could fill two swimming pools.

4

foundational movement
Shoulder Press

with PVC pipe head back
Push PVC straight up
Keep lazers low
Keep dumbbell inline with ears

NO DIP · PRESS UP.

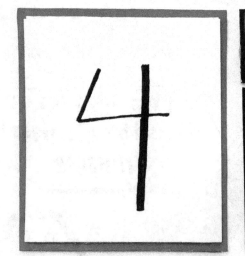

9 min EMOM

1.) Box Jumps

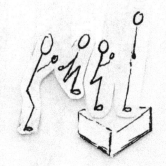

2.) Hollow Holds / Dead Bug
30 sec.

30 sec.

3.) Strict Press

We use our 5 main senses to take in information about the world around us.

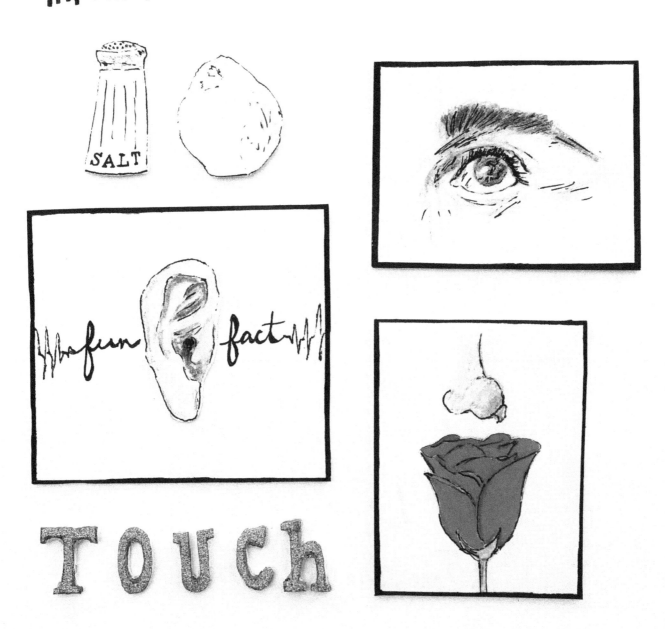

TOUCh

When one sense suffers the other senses are enhanced.

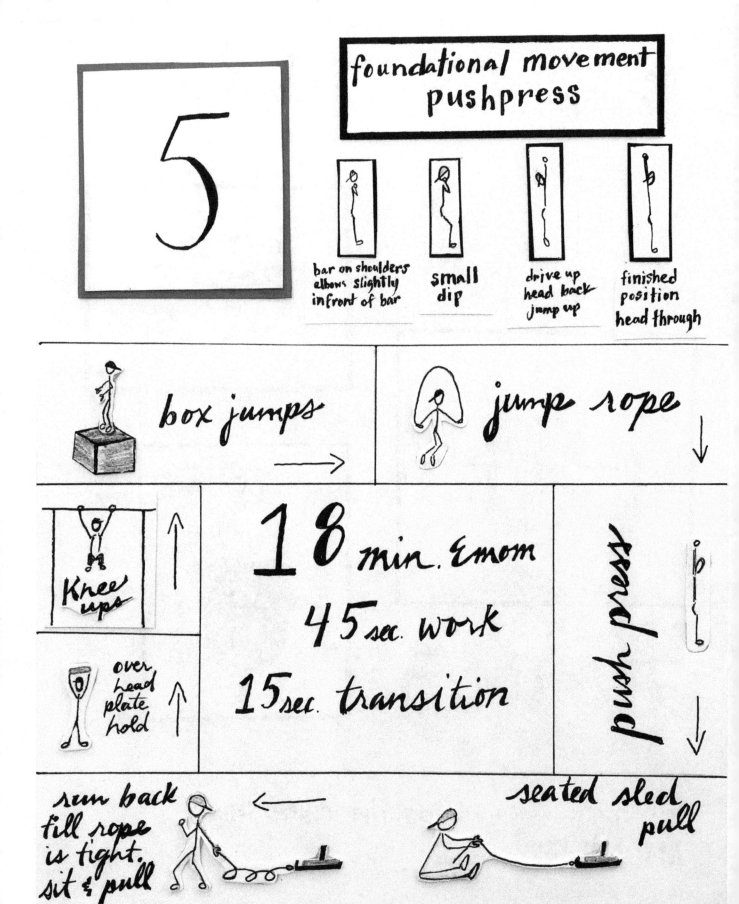

5

foundational movement
pushpress

bar on shoulders
elbows slightly
in front of bar

small
dip

drive up
head back
jump up

finished
position
head through

box jumps →

jump rope ↓

Knee ups ↑

over
head
plate
hold ↑

18 min. Emom
45 sec. work
15 sec. transition

push press ↓

run back
till rope
is tight.
sit & pull ←

seated sled
pull

Some examples of these are:

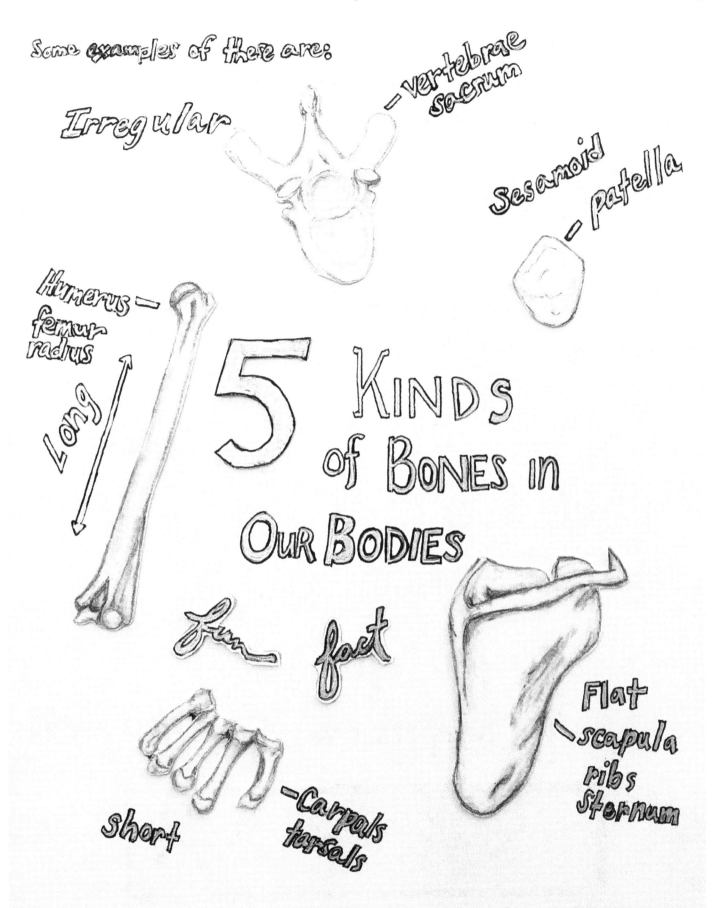

Irregular — Vertebrae
sacrum

Sesamoid — Patella

Humerus —
femur
radius

Long

5 KINDS of BONES in OUR BODIES

Fun fact

Short —Carpals
tarsals

Flat
—scapula
ribs
sternum

1 start   2 small   3 Jump   4 land in   5 stand to
               dip   punch   dip   full extension

3 rounds for time

10 push jerks

10 Burpees over bar/dumbbells

fun facts about our Lungs

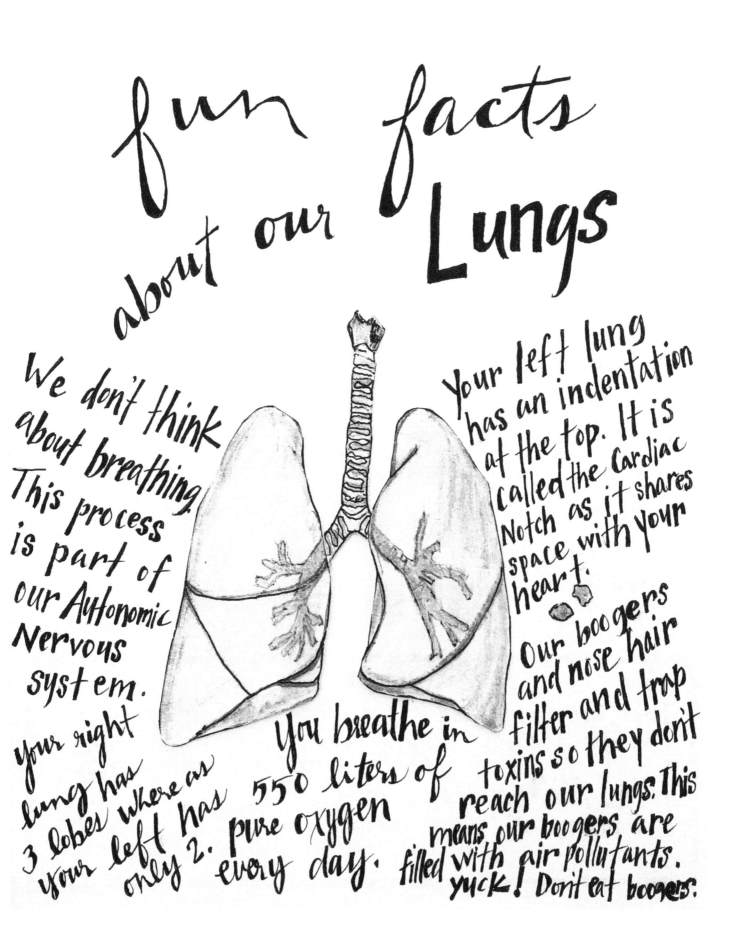

We don't think about breathing. This process is part of our Autonomic Nervous system.

your right lung has 3 lobes whereas your left has only 2.

You breathe in 550 liters of pure oxygen every day.

Your left lung has an indentation at the top. It is called the Cardiac Notch as it shares space with your heart.

Our boogers and nose hair filter and trap toxins so they don't reach our lungs. This means our boogers are filled with air pollutants. yuck! Don't eat boogers.

7

foundational movement
deadlift

- Keep back straight.
- squeeze shoulder blades together.
- Try and bend bar.
- squeeze glutes as you stand.

The deadlift movement is a lot like rowing. Try this fun game, it's called "Rowling". It is a combination of bowling and rowing. You want to get a "strike". To do this you need to land on 100m. If you are under or over even by 1 or 2, thats how many air squats you do.

Did you know that your back has many layers of muscles?

Traps and Lats help keep your shoulders back during the deadlift.

Your traps and lats are extrinsic muscles otherwise known as secondary muscles.

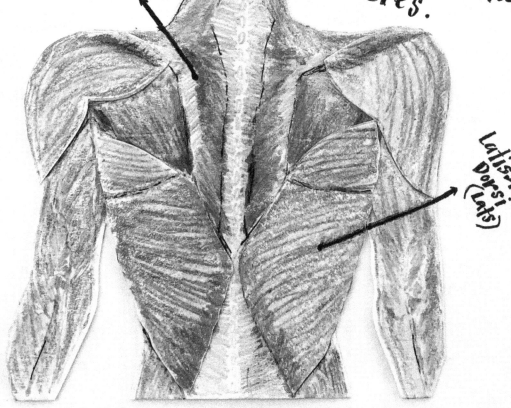

Trapezius (Traps)

Latissimus Dorsi (Lats)

fun fact

Sumo

Deadlift Highpull

"SDLHP"

foundational movement

This movement gets its name from this guy and his wide stance.

15, 12, 9

15 SDLHP
15 Burpees

clap over head

12 SDLHP
12 Burpees
9 SPLHP
9 Burpees

Grip with thumbs touching, wrap hands around bar. Stance should be a little wider than that of deadlift, and comfortable.

smile

* children begin losing their baby teeth around 6 years old.

* Try and brush your teeth twice a day.

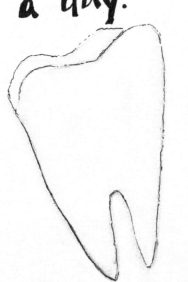

fun fact
FLOSS

MINT
WAXED

my dad used to say... "You don't have to floss all your teeth, just the ones you want to keep."

Flossing your teeth once per day can help prevent stinky breath and remove any food that is stuck between teeth.

9

foundational movement
MED BALL CLEAN

10 min.   AMRAP

10 air squats

10 butterfly sit-ups

100m Run

10 med ball cleans

1 rep.

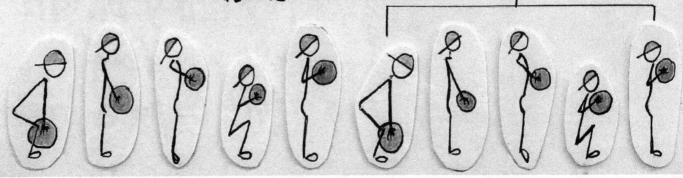

Did you Know that your words have the power to grow things ?

fun fact

You are Awesome

stupid

* Experiments have proven that with your words you can grow or Kill a plant
* With our words we can build people up or tear them down

Let us scatter seeds of Kindness with our words and not only grow plants but let us also grow friendships.

Practice speaking kind words today.

chapter

2

10 General Physical Skills

10 General Physical Skills

Some people are good at a few of these skills. But, to be proficient at all 10 will take work. Let us take time and work on these skills.

endurance
stamina
flexibility
strength
power
speed
coordination
agility
balance
accuracy

These are organic.

observable changes in your body.

They come about by training.

Both are adaptations of training and practice.

Neurological changes in the body will come about through practice.

endurance — The ability of body systems to gather process and deliver oxygen.

RUN/BIKE/ROW

stamina — The ability of body systems to process, deliver, store, and utilize energy.

HIGH REPITITION PUSH UPS

strength — The ability of a muscular unit, or combination of muscular units, to apply force.

BENCH PRESS
DEAD LIFT
BACK SQUAT

flexibility — The ability to maximize the range of motion at a given joint.

SQUATTING BELOW PARALLEL

power — The ability of a muscular unit or a combination of muscular units to apply force in minimum time.

OLYMPIC LIFTS
CLEAN/JERK/SNATCH

speed — The ability to minimize the time cycle of a repeated movement.

SPRINTS

coordination — The ability to combine several distinct movement patterns into a singular distinct movement.

DOUBLE UNDERS

agility — The ability to minimize transition time from one movement pattern to another.

BOX JUMPS

balance — The ability to control the placement of the body's center of gravity in relation to its base.

OVER HEAD SQUAT

accuracy — The ability to control movement in a given direction or at a given intensity.

WALL BALL

10

LET'S GO 4 A RUN

An Ultra IronMan runner once told me that to increase my running endurance I should run for time and not distance.
Use the chart below and try it out.

M	T	W	TH	F	S	SU
10 min	10 min	10 min	15 min	10 min	10 min	Rest
10 min	10 min	10 min	15 min	10 min	10 min	Rest
15 min	15 min	15 min	20 min	15 min	15 min	Rest
15 min	15 min	15 min	20 min	15 min	15 min	Rest
20 min	20 min	20 min	15 min	20 min	20 min	Rest
20 min	20 min	20 min	15 min	20 min	20 min	Rest

Run 6 days
Rest 1 day

Try and run without your feet making noise.

800m Run
rest 2 min
800m Run

fun fact

grab 'n' go

Healthy snacks give your body energy.

- If you want a car to run well you need good quality gasoline to fuel your engine.
- The same goes for your body. For you to perform well your body needs healthy snacks. Try adding at least one healthy snack a day to give you the energy you need.

11

T
E
A
M

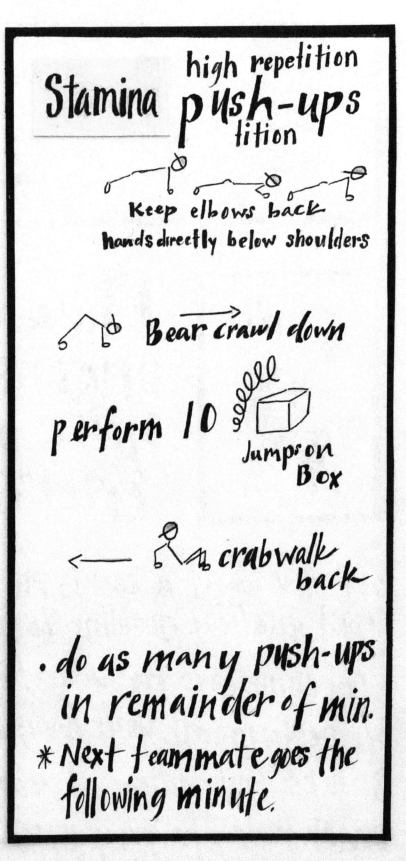

Stamina   high repetition push-ups

Keep elbows back
hands directly below shoulders

Bear crawl down

perform 10   Jump on Box

← crabwalk back

. do as many push-ups in remainder of min.
* Next teammate goes the following minute.

Did you know that kids 9-12 years old need 9-11 hours of sleep every night?

- muscles are repaired while you sleep.
- enough sleep can boost your immunity.
- sleep can affect your mood.
- enough sleep refreshes emotions.
- sleep increases brain function, helping your ability to learn.

fun fact

12

flexibility

When you can maximize the range of motion at a given joint, you have a great deal of flexibility.

· stretching and working on mobility will increase your flexibility.

Here are some stretches to try, to increase your flexibility.

half pigeon

low lunge

quad stretch

your rib cage is also called your Thorax. YOU HAVE 12 PAIRS OF RIBS

YOUR RIBS PROTECT YOUR VITAL ORGANS, THE HEART & LUNGS.

The back of your ribs connect to your Thoracic spine.

fun fact you have 2 pairs of floating ribs

GIRLS have a shorter sternum, which is the front long part of rib cage.

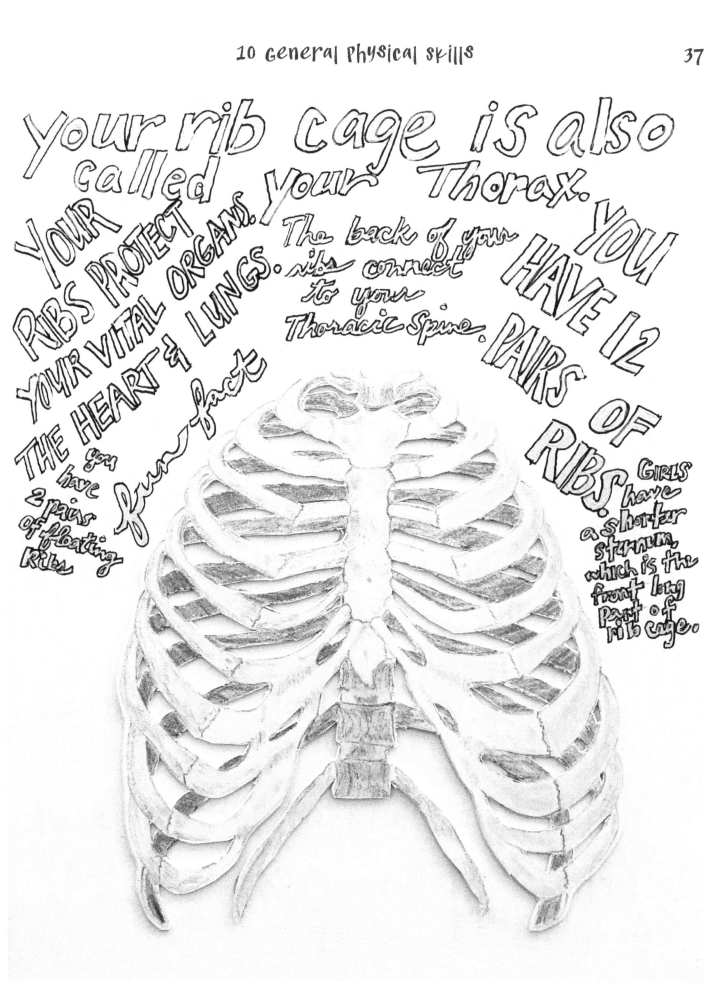

13

step by step positions

The snatch is all about **POWER**

- Olympic lifters apply maximum force to move weight in the shortest amount of time, to achieve the snatch, as well as other olympic lifts.

- strength and power are often confused because they are so similar, as they both apply force.

strength is nothing fast, just raw, brute force.

bench press

dead lift

back squat

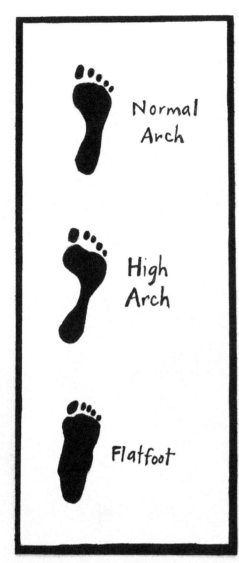

Normal Arch

High Arch

Flatfoot

fun fact

Are you wearing the right kind of shoes? your arches tell you a lot.

Normal - your arches can absorb and distribute the impact of walking and other activity.

High - your feet have an extra hard time absorbing impact and need extra cushioning.

Flat - causes your feet to roll inward, which is great for shock but not good on knees. add support with heel seats.

What kind of arch do you have?

Normal Arch   High Arch   Flat foot

14 Speed

Increasing our speed takes both training and practice.

- here are a few ways to get faster.
- try landing on the balls of your feet for a faster stride.

Sprints and ladder drills

 sprint to cone ⟶
rest one minute and repeat 5x

Ladder
sprint down and back from each cone

rest one minute and repeat 5x

Wall high knees

- 45 degree angle
- Press into wall
- quick feet
- high knees

15 sec. with band just above knees.
12 sec. without.
Try this 5 times
2-3 times a week.

fastest fact

... and the winners are,

• The fastest animal in the animal kingdom is the peregrine falcon -

• fastest reflexes only 1 animal can evade a cobra strike

speeds over 200 mph

mongoose

1st

fastest land animal

cheetah

The cheetah usually gets the credit for being the fastest... but he has competition

15

DOUBLE UNDERS

TEAM
chipper

1000m ROW

800 Jump ropes

600m RUN as a team

400m ROW

200 Jump ropes

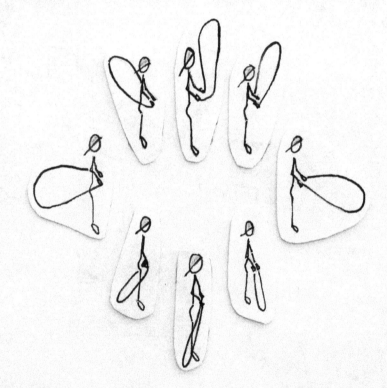

- jump tall   - stay relaxed
- keep legs straight
- flick wrist twice to jump rope 2x
coordination & practice

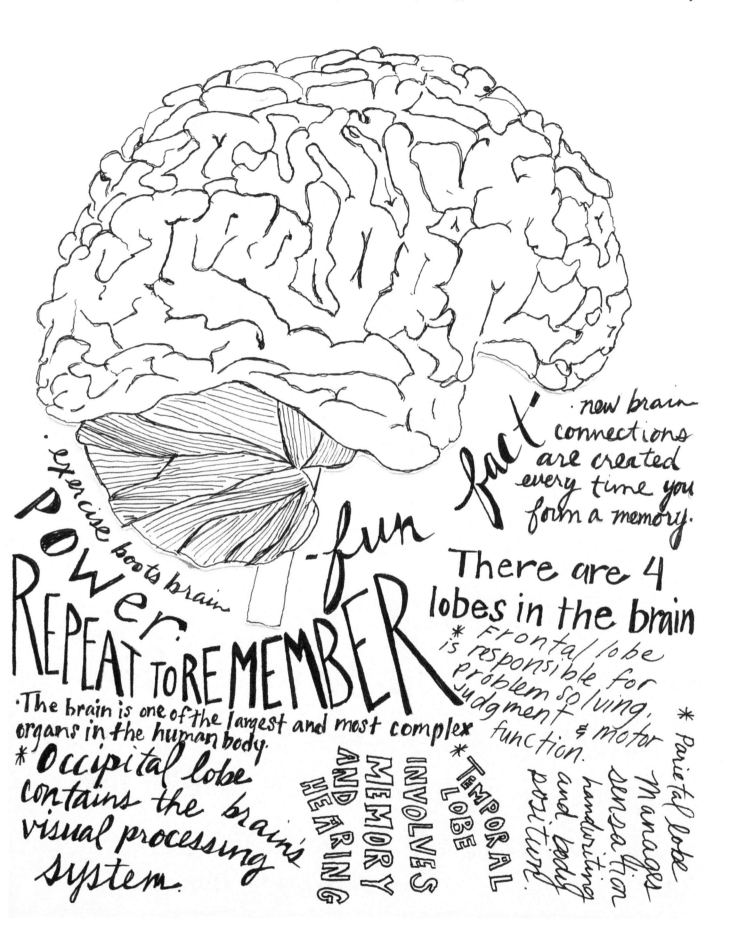

. new brain connections are created every time you form a memory.

- fun fact

exercise boots brain

POWER.

REPEAT TO REMEMBER

There are 4 lobes in the brain

* Frontal lobe is responsible for problem solving, judgment & motor function.

* Parietal lobe manages sensation, handwriting, and body position.

. The brain is one of the largest and most complex organs in the human body.

* Occipital lobe contains the brain's visual processing system.

* TEMPORAL LOBE INVOLVES MEMORY AND HEARING

16 | agility

agility is all about your ability to minimize transition time from one movement pattern to another. Working on Box Jumps is one way to practice this skill.

10 Box Jumps

* What we are looking for with this movement is how quickly you can transition from jumping to landing to jumping again.

- Time yourself doing 10 Box Jumps. Do this again to see if you can quicken your transitions.

fun fact

Our hair color and type are a part of our unique design.
This and other physical attributes link us to people in our family line. It is hereditary and can be passed down from parent to child.

* Melanin in the hair shaft also determines hair color.

* hair greys or gets lighter in color as shaft runs out of melanin.

17

Balance

The ability to control the placement of the body's center of gravity in relation to its base.

over-head squat

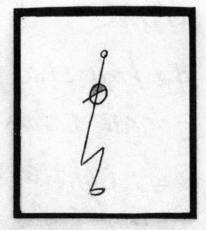

Balance takes practice

zero gravity in space fun fact

gravity

The Earth's gravitational pull is an invisible force that causes objects to pull towards the earth's center.

* Learn about Sir Isaac Newton and his 3 laws of motion on the internet. Ask a parent or gaurdian for help when searching on the web. Here is a safe kids site.

<https://surfnetkids.com/resources/isaac-newton/

18

accuracy

The wall ball movement is a great way to work on your accuracy.

- accuracy helps you control movement in a given direction or intensity.

- throw the ball up at the target and catch the ball as you go back down into a squat.

Practice 10, then 20.

WALL BALL

accuracy

Did you know that sharks and humans have the same 5 senses?

fun fact

sharks have 2 more!

- The shark's lateral line helps detect pressure variations in the water.
- The Electroreception sense is made up of hundreds of gel filled pores located around the shark's nose. These pores help detect electrical current in the water. This helps the shark locate its prey by tracking the fish's heart beat.

I've been growing in my faith since I was a kid, and I've come to realize that faith can't be seen. Faith has to be experienced. Faith takes action. You have to believe in order to experience or even see faith. I've also learned that faith in someone or something takes trust. And getting through the devastation of losing my dad would take loads of trust. I believe that since God helped me through so many hard times in my past He would do it again. my experience, because I know and trust God, is that He is always faithful to carry me through the hard times. God has a winning track record in my life, not only for me but also for all who put their trust in Him.

chapter

3

strength and development

Muscular Strength
- ## endurance
- ## Power

muscular strength

- The primary benefit of increasing muscle strength is that it improves performance and our overall physical fitness.

- Building muscle strength takes time.

- Muscular strength is primarily gauged by the maximum amount of weight that any given muscle can move for one repetition.

endurance

- a large portion of muscular strength is endurance, which is the muscle's ability to repeat the contraction for a longer period of time before becoming fatigued.

- muscular strength is increased by performing gradual resistance training over time to improve the endurance of the muscle.

power

- muscular power is the ability to generate as much force as possible as quickly as possible.

- when the muscles in the body are used to perform high intensity movements in short bursts, power is used.

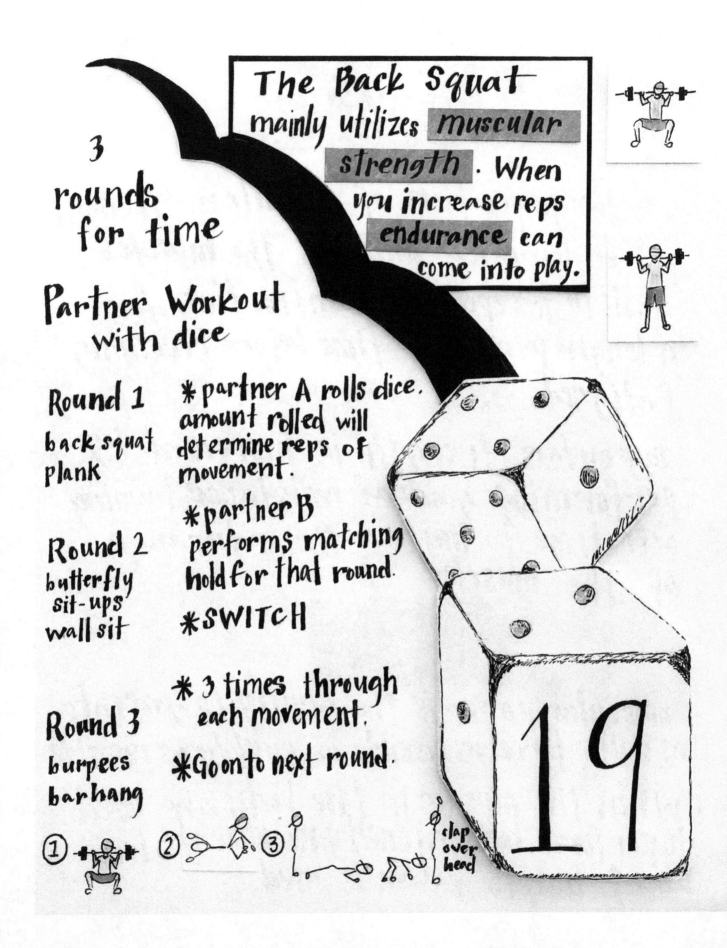

The Back Squat mainly utilizes **muscular strength**. When you increase reps **endurance** can come into play.

3 rounds for time

Partner Workout with dice

Round 1
back squat
plank

Round 2
butterfly
sit-ups
wall sit

Round 3
burpees
bar hang

* partner A rolls dice. amount rolled will determine reps of movement.

* partner B performs matching hold for that round.

* SWITCH

* 3 times through each movement.

* Go on to next round.

① ② ③ clap over head

19

fun fact

Did you know that there are 17 teaspoons of sugar in one 20oz bottle of soda?

consuming too much sugar can be
TOXIC - ADDICTIVE - DEADLY
and can cause:

- insulin resistance and obesity
- depletion of vitamins and minerals
- cardiovascular disease, liver disease cancer, arthritis, and gout

20

Strict Pull-ups require a great deal of ==muscular strength== and ==endurance==.

Practice doing negatives to strengthen your strict pull-up.

jump & hold chin above bar

slowly lower body under the bar

finish at full extension under bar

Workout

6 minute Amrap
4 strict pull-ups or 3 negatives
6 Butterfly sit-ups
100 meter run

How long can you hold above bar for?

Did you Know that there are 7 types of joints in our bodies that differ by function?

This is your shoulder joint. Ball and socket.

fun fact

A joint is where 2 bones touch.

21

Sled Pulls utilize POWER

Sled PULL

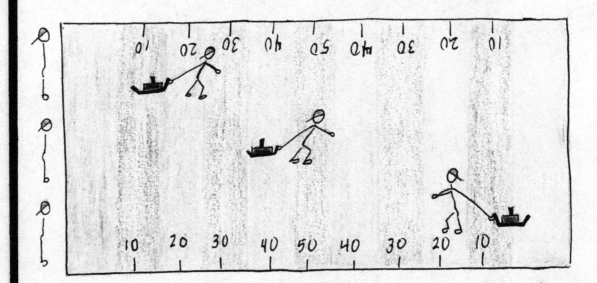

Partner A goes down & back while Partner B rests. switch. Go for 18 min.
*use 25-pound plate

fun facts

about your

KIDNEYS

your kidneys process and filter 50 gallons of blood every day.

They filter and remove water waste from your body.

Kidneys make an active form of vitamin D.

you can live a normal healthy life with only 1 kidney.

22

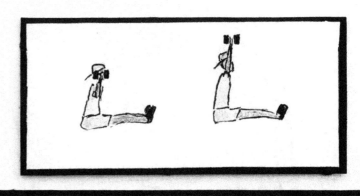

Seated Dumbbell Press

muscular strength

endurance

45 sec. of work 15 sec. transition for 16 minutes each station four times

After my dad died, I felt like I was in a dark hole. I was depressed and in a rut. I work far away from my biological family and see them several times a year, so being single is hard to establish family far from home. What I experienced in that *family* season of just losing my dad was very special. The people I work with something who are dear friends of mine invited me in. I felt seen. I could grieve. I could be me. I began to feel like I belonged. My fitness community has become like family. I know I'm always welcome and there's always a place for me at the table.

chapter

$\boxed{4}$

gymnastics

Gymnastics

If you perform gymnastics movements properly, they influence every aspect of your life, and have a dramatic effect on your fitness.

Gymnastics will help in our developing many of the 10 General Physical skills.

Gymnastics training produces impressive strength gains.

Strength

strength is a must to perfect proper form. You will eventually master the movement if you keep at it and this

Process will make you stronger.

Try not to rush these movements.

As strength is required for proper form, proper form is required to demonstrate body control.

Body Control

Body control helps us stay in position longer and strengthens our core stability. This ability will help us with other movements. Stabilizing our core takes practice.

23

Practicing Handstands and these other holds takes a great deal of Body Control.

log rolls

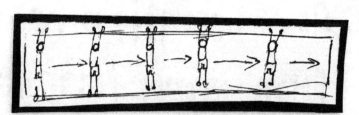

try rolling on a mat or grass

forward rolls

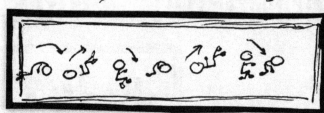

Tabata

20 seconds work

10 seconds rest

hollow hold

scissor Kicks

hollow rocks

2 minutes each movement

fun facts about our Muscles

Our muscles are uniquely made to move when we move. They all have very specific jobs.

Gluteus Maximus
- stand
- jump
- climb

Bicep
- Pulls toward your body

Tricep
- pushes away from your body

Quadriceps
- helps to extend leg

Hamstring
- helps to stand and jump.

Pectorals
- swings arm back
- used when swinging a racket

24 Tight body stabilization on bar

*ab rolls down mat keeping a tight core.

Tabata → Hollow Holds 2 min.
20 sec. work
10 sec. rest

How long can you hold on?

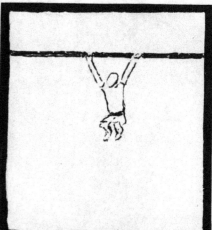

core stability

BAR WARS

Body control

Did you know that Grip strength takes practice?

Grip can be a limiting factor for your performance, or lack thereof on many exercises.
Here are some ways to work on grip and hand strength.

 hand grippers

 hand stands

BAR HANGS

 plate Pinches

fun *fact*

25

Skill: Kipping Technique

Hollow
- While pulling down on bar bring rib cage to your belly.
- point toes and lift legs slightly.

Arch
- pull arms behind you, sending head through.
- Keep core tight by squeezing everything.
- use hips to drive forward
- point toes

body control

Minute Work

① Pike push-up   ② barhang   ③ jumping Jacks

3 rounds

1 minute each movement

- Sun fact -

exposure to the sun should be done slowly.
Avoid sunburn by building up your tolerance SLOWLY.

* Sunlight builds the immune system.
* Regular sunlight exposure increases the growth and height in children
* Sunlight increases OXYGEN content in human blood.
* Sunlight can cure depression.
  Getting outside can change your mood

can you do the "worm"?

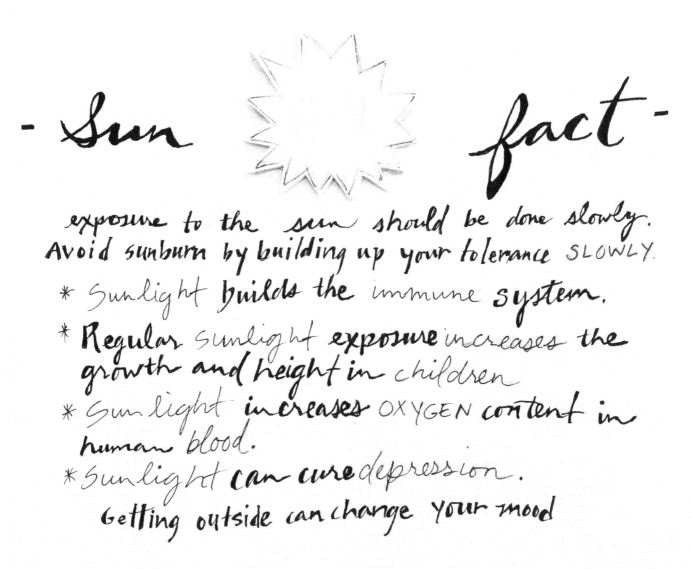

get upside down

practice walking on your hands
and doing handstands

26

core stability

SuperHero Holds

hold for **25** seconds
REST AND REPEAT

strength is utilized to maintain these holds and perform hand stand walks.

hollow holds

hand stand walks

your core is not just your abs. but is also made up of side and back muscles. All these muscles are necessary to engage, to perform safe movement. Pull your rib cage down and pull your belly button into your spine. —squeeze—

Three muscle Types

① skeletal

✱These are **voluntary muscles**
- Diaphragm, which assists us in breathing
- muscles of limbs
- other muscles associated with movement.

fun

② smooth

✱ These are involuntary muscles. They work without you thinking about it.
- Blood vessels, organs.
- other muscles associated with sustaining life.

fact

③ Cardiac

✱ This muscle is involuntary and it's the only one.

your heart

27

Arch   Hollow   Pull-up   Push away from Bar   Arch

Skill: Kipping pull-up

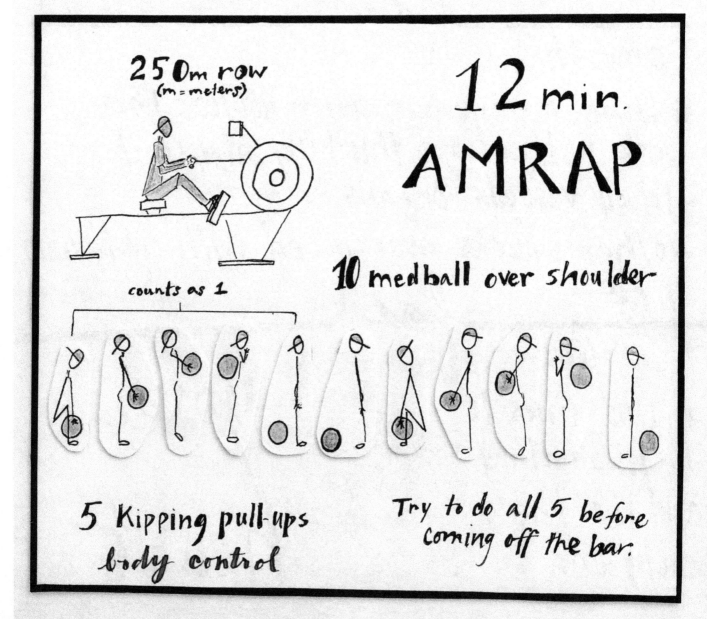

250m row
(m = meters)

12 min.
AMRAP

counts as 1

10 medball over shoulder

5 Kipping pull-ups
body control

Try to do all 5 before
coming off the bar.

Have you bumped your funny bone before? Me too!

- Did you know that the funny bone isn't actually a bone but a nerve?

- This nerve is the largest unprotected nerve in the human body, so when bumped you feel an electric shock-like sensation.

- It's really called the Ulnar nerve as it runs along the Ulnar bone.

- The "Funny bone" name is thought to be a pun, based on the "humerus" bone and the word "humorous".

fun fact

— humerus bone

ulnar bone

ulnar nerve

radius bone

There have been many moments in my life that I have quit whatever I was doing because it was hard. But there was a moment where that thought process changed for me. That moment happened to be in the middle of a workout. I had the thought that, if I just didn't — do all

integrity

the pushups, no one would know. I could simply walk away without finishing, slip out and not be noticed. But I just couldn't do it because of the integrity of those who were in the gym. I had a revelation that me quitting here, because it was hard, was something that I had done in every area of my life. I had to finish. Breaking this cycle was a defining moment and has a lot to do with this book being published.

chapter

$$\boxed{5}$$

skill work

Skill

- In order to improve our fitness, we need to work on the things that are challenging.

- We don't get overall fit when we only work on the movements we love or do well.

■ working on our weaknesses will help us in our overall health as well as fitness.

■ When we challenge ourselves, we are giving ourselves the opportunity to grow and get better at many things.

■ Look at areas you are weak in and make a plan to improve in those areas.

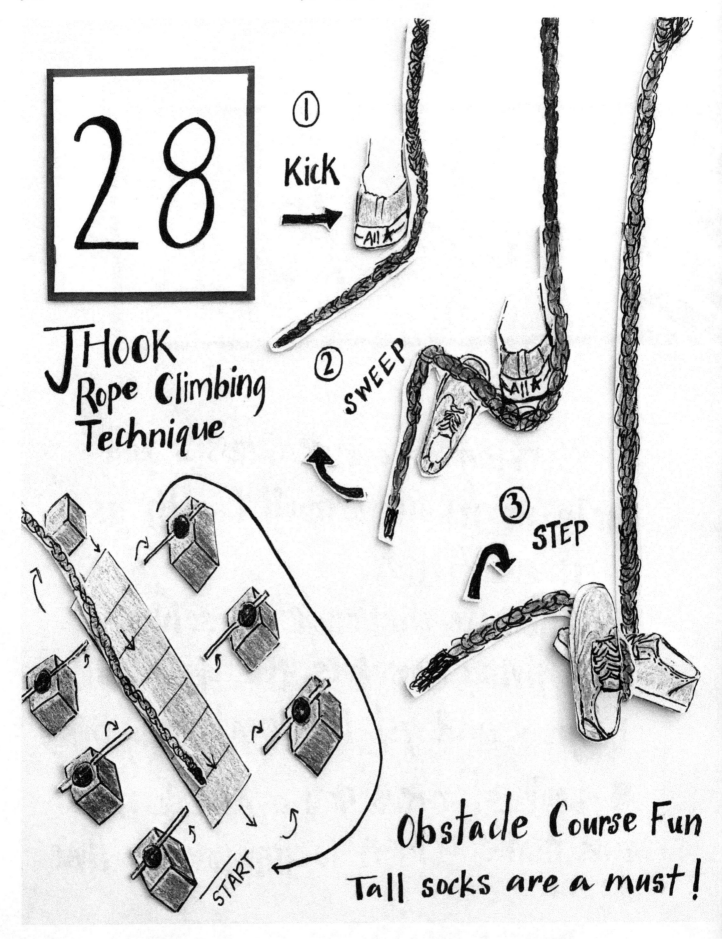

28

① Kick

② SWEEP

③ STEP

JHook
Rope Climbing
Technique

Obstacle Course Fun
Tall socks are a must!

START

Did you know that rubbing a balloon against your hair creates

STATIC ELECTRICITY?

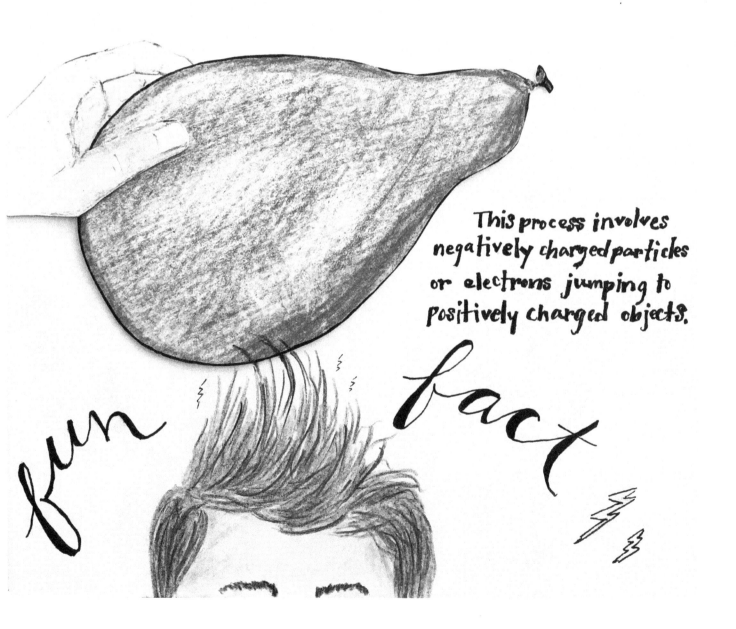

This process involves negatively charged particles or electrons jumping to positively charged objects.

fun fact

29

3 ROUNDS FOR TIME

12 pistol squats
12 pike push-ups
100m run

PISTOL

Did you know that flamingos aren't naturally pink? They are born white!

They eat Brine shrimp, which is rich in a nutrient called Beta Carotene. This turns all their feathers deep pink.

And because their knee joint is faced backwards they are unable to do pistol squats.

- fun fact -

30

SKill: Toe 2 Bar

warm up your shoulders

stretch

Pull arm toward your body

give yourself a pat on the back & pull elbow toward other arm.

Hang on Bar

15 min AMRAP

7   Toe 2 Bar

6   air squats

5   push ups

100m Run

Your big toe has 2 bones whereas the others have 3 bones each

> 2

People without toes or other limbs find ways to OVERCOME

lose a thumb? No Problem

have it replaced with a big toe.

-fun facts-

Toes

Did you know that Toe wrestling is a real sport? could you be the next champion?

Polydactylism

a congenital condition that results in extra digits.

I have heard it said that love looks like something, and I believe that to be true. Love is more than telling someone, "I love you." It is more than saying, "I love Thai food" or "I love this sports team." Love is selfless. I have felt most loved when I feel seen. And when someone goes out of their way to make me special or love something let me know that they have been thinking about me, I feel loved. I know that if I were to fail miserably those closest to me would be there to help me pick up the broken pieces of my life. Love gives room to fail. I know that love is not dependent on my performance I can be fully me and that's okay.

References

page 8

"The 9 Foundational CrossFit Movements Every Athlete Should Know." *www.facebook.com/thecoachkshow*. April 23, 2020. https://athleticmuscle.net/crossfit-movements/. Accessed September 29, 2020.

page 11

"The Water in You: Water and the Human Body" (n.d.). https://water.usgs.gov/edu/propertyyou.html. Accessed September 18, 2020.

"Water Your Brain for Extra Gains." October 18, 2018. https://www.gritcityfitnessandperformance.com/water-your-brain-for-extra-gains/. Accessed September 18, 2020

page 13

"Facts about Blood and Blood Types." (n.d.). https://www.redcrossblood.org/donate-blood/blood-types.html?icid=rdrt-blood-types. Accessed September 18, 2020.

page 15

"50 Incredibly Weird Facts about the Human Body." (n.d.). https://bsnprogram.com/2010/50-incredibly-weird-facts-about-the-human-body/. Accessed September 18, 2020.

"What Is the Strongest Muscle in the Human Body?" (n.d.). https://www.loc.gov/everyday-mysteries/item/what-is-the-strongest-muscle-in-the-human-body/. Accessed September 18, 2020.

page 17

Bates, M. "Super Powers for the Blind and Deaf." *Scientific American*, September 18, 2012. https://www.scientificamerican.com/article/superpowers-for-the-blind-and-deaf/. Accessed September 18, 2020.

page 19

Briers, D. "Types of Bones in the Human Body Simplified." December 17, 2012. http://www.dbriers.com/tutorials/2012/12/types-of-bones-in-the-human-body-simplified/. Accessed September 18, 2020.

page 21

Craig Freudenrich, P. "How Your Lungs Work." October 6, 2000. https://health.howstuffworks.com/human-body/systems/respiratory/lung3.htm. Accessed September 18, 2020.

"How Much Oxygen Does a Person Consume in a Day?—Air Quality." (n.d.). *Discovery Health.* https://www.sharecare.com/health/air-quality/oxygen-person-consume-a-day. Accessed September 18, 2020.

Hurly, A. "Why Boogers Happen, and How to Get Rid of Them." November 14, 2017. 2020, from https://www.gq.com/story/how-to-get-rid-of-boogers. Accessed September 18, 2020.

"Lungs: Definition, Location, Anatomy, Function, Diagram, Diseases. " December 1, 2017. https://www.therespiratorysystem.com/lungs/. Accessed September 18, 2020.

page 23

Lecturio. "Extrinsic Back Muscles" *Anatomy Online: Medical Library.* January 21, 2020. 2020, from https://www.lecturio.com/magazine/allochthonous-back-muscles/. Accessed September 18, 2020.

page 25

"When Do Children Start Losing Baby Teeth?" August 14, 2019. https://www.mayoclinic.org/healthy-lifestyle/childrens-health/expert-answers/baby-teeth/faq-20058532. Accessed September 18, 2020.

page 27

Mind, T., & Mind, T. "Mindful Speech: The Word Power Experiment." February 7, 2012. https://thewholeheartedmind.wordpress.com/2012/01/31/mindful.speech-the-word-power-experiment/. Accessed September 18, 2020.

page 30

"10 General Physical Skills." August 3, 2015. https://crossfitaptos.com/2015/07/14/10-general-physical-skills/. Accessed September 18, 2020.

Page 33

Jeffrey, K. (2015, September 01). How to Fuel Your Body for Energy. Retrieved September 18, 2020, from https://www.active.com/nutrition/articles/how-to-fuel-your-body-for-energy?page=1. Accessed September 18, 2020.

Page 35

"Mood and Sleep." *Department of Health & Human Services.* April 5, 2017. https://www.betterhealth.vic.gov.au/health/HealthyLiving/Mood-and-sleep. Accessed September 18, 2020.

Maldarelli, C. (n.d.). "Why Do People Need to Sleep?" https://www.popsci.com/why-we-need-sleep/. Accessed September 18, 2020.

Warner, J. "Sleep Deprivation Stirs Up Emotions." October 22, 2017. https://www.webmd.com/sleep-disorders/news/20071022/sleep-deprivation-stirs-up-emotions. Accessed September 18, 2020.

Page 37

Iazzetti, G. (2009) *Human Anatomy.* Cobham, Surrey:TAJ Books International LLP. Accessed September 18, 2020.

Page 39

"Do You Know Your Foot Arch Type? Take the Test and Find Out." July 28, 2020. from https://heelthatpain.com/foot-arch-type-test/. Accessed September 19, 2020.

Page 41

"Fastest Animals." September 5, 2020. https://en.m.wikipedia.org/wiki/Fastest_animals. Accessed September 18, 2020.

Mohammed, S. "Which Animal Has Better Reflexes, a Mongoose or a Cat?" May 4, 2018. https://www.quora.com/which-animal-has-better-reflexes-a-mongoose-or-a-cat. Accessed September 18, 2020.

Page 43

Burnett, D. "What Happens in Your Brain When You Make a Memory?" *The Guardian.* September 16, 2015. https://www.theguardian.com/education/2015/sep/16/what-happens-in-your-brain-when-you-make-a-memory. Accessed September 19, 2020.

Hoffman, M. "Brain (Human Anatomy): Picture, Function, Parts, Conditions, and More." *WebMd.* May 18, 2019. https://www.webmd.com/brain/picture-of-the-brain. Accessed September 19, 2020.

Parrish, S. "12 Things We Know about How the Brain Works." *The Week.* August 26, 2013. https://theweek.com/articles/460769/12-things-know-about-how-brain-works. Accessed September 18, 2020.

page 45

"Why Does Hair Turn Gray? (for Kids)." *Nemours KidsHealth.* (n.d.). https://kidshealth .org/en/kids/gray-hair.html. Accessed September 20, 2020.

page 47

Feldman, B. "Sir Isaac Newton." *Surfnet Kids.* December 31, 2019. https://www .surfnetkids.com/resources/sir-isaac-newton/. Accessed September 20, 2020.

page 49

"Lateral Line." (n.d.). https://www.sharks-world.com/?s=lateral+line. Accessed September 20, 2020.

Long, B. "How Sharks and Other Animals Evolved Electroreception to Find Their Prey." https://phys.org/news/2018-02-sharks-animals-evolved-electroreception-theirprey.html. Accessed September 20, 2020.

page 54

"The Difference Between Muscular Strength & Muscular Endurance." (n.d.). https:// www.livestrong.com/article/154326-the-difference-between-muscular-strength -muscular-endurance/. Accessed September 21, 2020.

Quinn, E. (n.d.). "Simple Methods for Improving Muscular Endurance." https://www .verywellfit.com/what-is-muscular-endurance-3120360. Accessed September 21, 2020.

page 55

"Strength Training versus Power Training." (n.d.). https://www.physio-pedia.com /Strength_Training_versus_Power_Training. Accessed September 21, 2020.

Puma, Dr. John La Puma. "How Many Teaspoons of Sugar Are in a Coke?" May 15, 2020. from https://www.drjohnlapuma.com/vitamins-and-supplements/how-many -teaspoons-of-sugar-are-in-a-coke-2/. Accessed September 29, 2020.

page 57

"Effects of Consuming Too Much Sugar." (n.d.). https://articles.mercola.com/sugar-side-effects.aspx. Accessed September 29, 2020.

page 59

Iazzetti, G. *Human Anatomy.* TAJ Books International, LLP. Cobham, Surrey: 2009.

page 61

5 Interesting Facts About the Kidney. (2020, January 24). Retrieved September 29, 2020, from https://www.dmclinicalresearch.com/5-interesting-facts-about-the-kidney/.

page 63

Do Taste Buds Really Cover All Our Tastes?!?! What Else Matters?? *Hummusgirl's Blog.* June 2, 2014. https://hummusgirl.com/2014/04/24/do-the-taste-buds-really-cover-all-our-tastes/. Accessed September 18, 2020.

page 68

"Gymnastics Training Guide" Crossfit.com. 2015. https://assets.crossfit.com/pdfs/seminars/SMERefs/Gymnastics/GymnasticsCourse_SeminarGuide.pdf. Accessed September 29, 2020.

page 71

"Major Muscles and Their Functions" (n.d.) https://quizlet.com/19826934/major-muscles-their-function-flash-cards. Accessed September 29, 2020.

page 73

Velazquez, Eric N., October 9, 2012. "Improve Your Grip." https://www.theboxmag.com/crossfit-training/get-a-grip-9533. Accessed September 29, 2020.

page 75

"Sunlight for Health." (n.d.). https://www.sunislife.com/sunlight-for-health/. Accessed September 29, 2020.

"Summer Sunlight Exposure Increases Growth in Children." November 2, 105. https://sunlightinstitute.org/summer-sunlight-exposure-increases-growth-in-children/. Accessed September 29, 2020.

page 77

"What Are Three Different Types of Muscles?" (n.d.). https://www.answers.com/Q/what_are_three_different_types_of_muscles. Accessed September 29, 2020.

page 79

"Ulnar Nerve." August 28, 2020. https://en.m.wikipedia.org/wiki/Ulnar_nerve. Accessed September 29, 2020.

page 87

"Electricity." (n.d.). https://www.ducksters.com/science/static_electricity.php. Accessed September 29, 2020.

page 89

Helmenstine, Anne Marie P. (n.d.) "Why Are Flamingos Pink?" April 7, 2019. https://www.thoughtco.com/why-are-flamingos-pink-607870. Accessed September 29, 2020.

page 91

"How Many Bones Are in a Human's Big Toe?" (n.d.)https://www.answers.com/Q/How_many_bones_are_in_a_humans_big_toe. Accessed September 29, 2020.

Knowlab. Vujicic: Life without Limbs." June 3, 2019. https://knowlab.in/nick-vujicic-life-without-limbs/. Accessed September 29, 2020.

"9 Toe-tally Cool Facts." December 22, 2008. https://www.mentalfloss.com/article/20422/9-toe-tally-cool-facts. Accessed September 29, 2020.

About the Author

Erin Crain discovered her love for kids and fitness at a CrossFit Kids' Training seminar in December of 2016, where she earned her CFL1 CrossFit Kids certification. From there, she began teaching fitness classes for first through eighth graders. That was when she realized she would need to make fun activities and learning experiences for her classes, as she did not have access to the kind of curriculum she knew she (and they) needed. Kid Fit for Fun is the product of that first year with the kids!

For more information or to order more books, you can contact Erin through her website at www.kidfitforfun.com.

CPSIA information can be obtained
at www.ICGtesting.com
Printed in the USA
LVHW061437110221
679057LV00005B/361

9 781952 943034